My Best Nest: A Purple Martin Story
© 2009 Rebecca Dellinger

Manufactured in the United States of America.

For information, please contact:

The P3 Press
16200 North Dallas Parkway, Suite 170
Dallas, Texas 75248

www.thep3press.com

972-381-0009

A New Era in Publishing™

ISBN-13: 978-1-933651-48-4
ISBN-10: 1-933651-48-2
LCCN: 2008909425

Author contact information:

Ree Dellinger

www.purplemartinstory.org

About the Author

Ree Dellinger earned a master's degree in biology studying Blue Jays and is a former science teacher. She has worked as an aviculturist and zoo registrar. As an aviculturist, she helped rear a diminutive Collared Sunbird on a diet of house spiders and fruit flies. Dressed in a crane costume she was a parent to magnificent Whooping Cranes and Siberian Cranes. Learn about cranes at www.operationmigration.org and www.savingcranes.org. For over thirty years, the author assisted her father in the care of his martin colony and served as a sub-permittee in his decades-long study of martins for the US Bird Banding Laboratory. The pieces of nesting material shown on the book's cover are drawn from items found in the nests of Purple Martins. Her father grew up on a small farm during the Great Depression. He was a gentle, considerate man who was an analytical thinker. He valued family, education, nature, hard work and the sciences. Taking care to do things safely and well was important to him. A portion of the story in this book has the mother bird thinking about potential hazards and contemplating how she will take precautions. In addition to eliciting discussions about migratory birds, the author hopes that teachers and parents may also use this book as a tool to initiate a discussion with children about safety.

About the Contributors

Joe Dellinger is a geophysicist. He uses a 35 mm camera mounted on an Astrophysics "Traveler" astronomical telescope at prime focus for his martin photography.

James R. Hill III earned a master's degree in ecology studying Barn Swallows. He is the founder and executive director emeritus of the Purple Martin Conservation Association and former editor of the "Purple Martin Update." He has traveled to Brazil four times to study Purple Martins in their winter range.

My Best Nest: A Purple Martin Story

Written and illustrated by Ree Dellinger
Photographs by Joe Dellinger and James R. Hill III
Endorsed by the Purple Martin Landlords of North Texas

www. purplemartinstory. org

Purple Martin Landlords
Of North Texas
*"Spreading the Word About this
Wonderful Bird"*

Dedication

This book is for the Purple Martins and the generations of martin guardians, especially my father and mother, and in memory of the conservationists Mr. and Mrs. Ernest Harold Baynes, and Esther Heacock.

Acknowledgements

Following the spirit of the Migratory Bird Treaty Act the writer, illustrator, and photographers contributed their efforts to this book solely for the benefit of promoting Purple Martins. Countless Purple Martins have contributed to this book as four decades of experiences with Purple Martins and hundreds of martin photographs were referenced to create this book.

Special thanks are due my parents and brother for the conception of the book, their encouragement in its development and access to their collections of martin photographs. The idea for *My Best Nest* started with the finding of a tiny scrap of blue fabric in a martin nest. Embroidered on this tiny piece of fabric was a half-inch unicorn.

Thanks are due the staffs of the US Bird Banding Laboratory (BBL), the Texas Parks and Wildlife Department, the Pennsylvania Game Commission, the Purple Martin Conservation Association (PMCA), The Nature Society, The Purple Martin Society and the Purple Martin Landlords of North Texas. Individual thanks are due Joe Dellinger, James R. Hill III, Charles Brown, Gisela Fregoe, Louise Chambers and BBL's Kathy Klimkiewicz.

Thanks and recognition are also given the following people: Bob Aram, Gordon Baker, Thomas Baynes, Thomas Becker, Lola Bravo, George Chapko, Tom Coulson, Kenny Crawford, Shirl Dellinger, Tad Dellinger, the Fiegenschue family, Esther Gallagher, Eleuterio de la Garza, Walt Hackfeld, Lis Hudson, Kent Justus, Mark Lackey, the Marma family, Karen Martin, Cliff May, Casey Patterson, the Pulich family, the Pyburn family, Carlyle Rogillio, George Sandusky, Terry Suchma, Ora Van Horn, the employees of the Highland Park Library and the staff of Brown Books Publishing.

"Cher-choo. Cher-choo."
I have things to do.

Spring's morning has come at last.
Today, I will begin my special task.

It is early dawn.
I open my bill and yawn.

My mate scratches to preen.
I survey the sunrise scene.

A cloudy morning greets me today.
Peek-a-boo, the clouds and sun will play.

I stretch both wings.
My mate cheerfully sings.

"Cher-choo, Cher-choo," I cry.
It is time to fly.

I jump from my house to sail on the wind.
Flapping my wings, I quickly ascend.

My mate, an avian ace, flies by my side
as I begin a most graceful glide.

While high in the sky,
for flying insects I spy.

For my breakfast I search,
while the wind is my perch.

I swoop and flutter
to catch a butterfly the color of butter.

As I continue my flight,
a beetle comes into sight.

The beetle is my delight,
for my mate a fly tastes right.

We stoop low to the east,
and continue to feast.

Finding breakfast for two,
I sing "Cher-choo, Cher-choo."

Rising high in the sky,
I catch a big, plump fly.

That delicious fly was juicy.
Now what else do I see?

Looking down,
I see the town.

High above the ground,
I see all around.

New houses have grown
next to a field a farmer has sown.

There is a new elementary school
that the students think is rather cool.

In the schoolyard children play every day
where a farmer used to bale his hay.

We fly over grassy fields blanketed in flowers,
and over pastures that have sprouted towers.

We fly over houses with swimming pools,
and yards where gardeners are working with tools.

Joining our friends, we swoop over tall trees.
Sailing above the rustling leaves we ride the gentle breeze.

Over the trees, we fly to the pond
of which we are very fond.

The pond is a popular spot.
My neighbors visit here a lot.

We do not need to stop.
We just skim the top.

Skimming with my bill,
I drink my fill.

After a long sip,
I take a quick dip.

With a calculated dash
I take a bath with a splash.

Breakfast is done and my energy surges.
Now to my special task my instinct urges.

Today, I start to build my nest.
I hope to make it my very best.

I have many places to go.
I want to hurry so.

20217979

But, I shall take my time.
Safety is also on my mind.

"Be careful," my thoughts ring
as I imagine each scary thing.

A car, hawk and cat,
I will have none of that.

"Do not go near the road!" when young I was told.
This my mother would fervently scold.

I know I will be mashed,
if by a car I get bashed.

I watch for a hungry hawk.
I know how they stalk.

With hawks and cats, I must have tact
so I will always have time to react.

A cat in the shadow I must see.
A hawk in a tree means danger to me.

If glare is in my eye,
I may not see what is nearby.

Martins have a special alarm.
We warn each other of possible harm.

We cry "Zweet, Zweet,"
when safety we seek.

As we go from place to place
we remember to keep a careful pace.

We will take great care
so we will not have a scare.

There are many things to find
to make my nest fine.

It will take a week
to find all that I seek.

One piece at a time, each time I carry.
Busy at work, I feel quite merry.

My mate knows how to please.
He brings small green leaves.

With caution, we look around
then we land on the ground.

I find a twig
that is not too big.

My mate finds a grass sprig,
where the gardener likes to dig.

In the schoolyard, I find a pencil stub
with an eraser that is worn to a nub.

Next, we fly to the lake
where I find mud to take.

Back and forth to our house we go.
After many trips our nest begins to grow.

To satisfy my hunger is now my need.
It is time again to feed.

I give my tail a little wag
and start to zig and zag.

I find several insects to nab
and one I know not to grab.

On we go for another sip and dip at the pond
where we martins enjoy our social bond.

Then we fly to a high wire
to adjust our feathered attire.

My mate and I sit in the sky
and visit with friends while we dry.

High on a wire we preen.
We keep our feathers very clean.

Next, I rest and sit in my nest.
I hope to make it my very best.

My mate stands guard singing with zest,
puffing out his glossy chest.

He stays alert
so we will not get hurt.

His feathers shine.
He looks mighty fine.

I listen to his lively melody.
His voice is filled with glee.

After my nap, I leap to the air.
"Cher-choo, Cher-choo," I call as if I had not a care.

I feed while happily on my way
to find a golden piece of hay.

We work into evening's dusk
feeling the urge that we must.

Sunset is ending.
Twilight is descending.

Our watchful neighbors await
as we arrive home a little late.

Seeing stars appear, we call it a day.
In our house we now stay.

Like my mate, I turn my head over my back.
I tuck my bill in feathers of blue and black.

Sleep is now what we seek.
This will be a busy week.

As twilight continues its descent,
we fall into sleep feeling very content.

Tomorrow we will work again on the nest.
I hope to make it my very best.

"Cher-choo. Cher-choo."
This I will do.

ABOUT PURPLE MARTINS

The songbirds in this story are Purple Martins, a species of swallow. The scientific name used by scientists everywhere for this species is *Progne subis*. Ornithologists recognize 83 species of swallows in the world. Swallows are insectivorous birds that specialize in eating flying insects. Purple Martins, at seven inches in size, are the largest swallow in North America.

Purple Martins winter in South America, mostly in Brazil. Purple Martins are a neo-tropical migratory songbird, and as such are protected by international law. Purple Martins return to the northern hemisphere to nest in the spring and early summer where the majority of the species nests in the eastern half of North America. A few Purple Martins nest in Mexico and the western half of North America.

One of the earliest scientific observers of Purple Martins was the Mexican clergyman, José Antonio Alzate Ramírez (1729-1799) who, aided by some of his parishioners, studied the Purple Martins nesting in his community of Ozumba, approximately forty-two miles north of Mexico City. Father Alzate was one of the first to conduct bird-banding studies.

Purple Martins in the eastern half of North America used to build nests in natural cavities such as abandoned woodpecker holes in hollow trees. Fortunately, centuries before the United States was established Native Americans began to provide Purple Martins with hollowed-out gourds hanging high from poles as nest sites so the birds would nest near their villages.

Figure 1. A male Purple Martin nesting in a hollowed-out natural gourd is shown giving his baby a dragonfly.
© James R. Hill III, Purple Martin Conservation Association.

As the European colonists cleared the old-growth trees of North America, the Purple Martins breeding in the eastern half of North America experienced a "tradition shift" and became dependent on man to provide them with hollowed-out gourds or special birdhouses as nesting sites. During the 1800s, it was popular to attract nesting Purple Martins to gourds and birdhouses in the South. The species was valued for its song and aerial displays. As a migratory species, Purple Martins were considered symbols of freedom.

In the western United States and Mexico, Purple Martins primarily use natural nest sites. Purple Martins nest in cavities in saguaro cacti in the Desert Southwest while in the mountain ranges of the western United States and coastal areas of the Pacific Northwest the species nests in cavities in trees such as aspen, pine and cottonwood. There are small, scattered populations nesting in California. If enough nest sites are available Purple Martins may form a colony of multiple nesting pairs.

Purple Martins suffer intense competition and harm from two introduced bird species, the European Starling, *Sturnus vulgaris*, and the European House Sparrow, *Passer domesticus*. These species were imported in the 1800s to North America from Europe and have widespread populations in North America. European Starlings are highly detrimental to native North American, cavity-nesting birds. The European House Sparrow species is declining in Europe and North America and is in peril in England.

Figure 2. European Starling.
© Joe Dellinger.

Figure 3. Male European House Sparrow.
© Joe Dellinger.

Female and juvenile Purple Martins have a dark-colored back and a white-colored belly. Female martins acquire a more sooty appearance to their belly feathers as they age. See figure 4.

Purple Martins molt (replace their feathers) once a year. During their first stay in South America young martins molt their juvenile plumage and grow their second-year plumage. The second-year plumage is similar to that of an adult female's, but many young males have some metallic blue-black feathers intermingled with the white feathers of the belly and throat. A second-year male is shown in figure 5.

Figure 5. Second-year male Purple Martin.
© Joe Dellinger.

Figure 4. An after-second-year female Purple Martin giving her feathers a good shake.
© Joe Dellinger.

Male Purple Martins over two years in age have a dark-colored back and a dark-colored belly. Males in this beautiful dark plumage are called after-second-year males. The dark body feathers are a metallic blue-black but may look blue or purple in some lighting conditions. The flight feathers will look black or brown depending on the lighting.

Some after-second-year males retain the white feather coloration on their legs, while others have gray or dark-colored feathers on their legs. An after-second-year male martin is shown in figure 6. He collected ant queens after a spring shower stimulated the ants to swarm.

Purple Martins build a shallow, cup-shaped nest inside their selected nest cavity. The birds collect twigs and short pieces of coarse grass to build their nests. Mud is also used when available. Martins place small green leaves in the nest bowl and use green leaves to cover their eggs. Both the male and female build the nest, but the female contributes more than the male to this activity. Both sexes defend the nest site. After the nest is complete, the female lays from three to six white eggs. The female does most of the incubating. Incubation lasts about 17 days. Both parents tend the young, which hatch naked and helpless. From the time the babies hatch until the time they are able to fly from the nest, the young martins are called nestlings.

Figure 6. After-second-year male Purple Martin.
© Joe Dellinger.

Figure 7. Purple Martin eggs and newborn nestlings.
© James R. Hill III, Purple Martin Conservation Association.

Figure 8. A mother Purple Martin bringing a meal to two of her young. © Joe Dellinger.

During food transfers both the parents and young protect their eyes by momentarily covering them with special membranes, called the nictitating membranes. These membranes function as safety glasses and may also be raised when a martin is scratching its head or capturing food. The nictitating membranes are drawn from the front of the eyes toward the back of the eyes. Purple Martins also have eyelids. Their eyelids are located at the lower part of their eyes and are drawn upward to close the eyes. The nictitating membranes are somewhat transparent and look bluish in photographs such as in figure 1.

Young martins fledge (leave the nest by flying away) when they are about 28 days old. Once they have flown, young martins are called fledglings. The parents continue to feed the young for a week or more after the young have fledged. The family often returns to the nest to sleep at night during this training period.

After the young are reared to independence, the adults and young begin to gather in roosts at night. A nocturnal roost is a location where birds gather to sleep and benefit from the increased safety of being in a group. Roosting martins usually sleep in trees, but when the roost is by a large body of water the martins often sleep underneath concrete highway bridges or in reed beds and thick brush growing on islands.

The number of birds gathering in a roost varies from a few hundred to several thousand. Think of a roost as a popular, seasonal bird motel with individual Purple Martins checking in and out of the bird motel on their own schedule. All the martins using a roost will arrive at the roost each evening about the same time, but when each bird first starts sleeping at the roost and stops sleeping at the roost is determined by each bird's individual schedule.

Small roosts used in one year may or may not be used in following years. Many of the larger roosts are used year after year. Larger roosts initially contain martins from local breeding colonies that have finished nesting for the year, but as martins begin to migrate a roost may contain martins that started their journey south in another town, state or Canada. Information about martin roost sites and their locations is being gathered by the Purple Martin Conservation Association (PMCA). To survive, roosting species must have safe roost sites.

Adult Purple Martins begin migrating south in the summer. Juveniles will be the last to migrate, with some not leaving until early fall. Purple Martins travel independently or in small, loose groups as they fly in migration. Purple Martins tend to be diurnal (daytime) migrants though they are capable of traveling at night. As Purple Martins are adapted to catch flying insects, they feed as they fly in migration.

Most migratory songbird species are not able to feed while flying and require places where they may stop and feed during the day after traveling at night. Nocturnal migrants are susceptible to impact injury and can become disoriented by artificial lighting. Studies to understand the influence and harm of various types of artificial lighting on our native fauna are ongoing. To learn about protecting the night sky visit www.darksky.org and www.nature.nps.gov/air/lightscapes.

All migratory birds require rest stops of natural habitat along their migration routes where they may "refuel" and rest without disturbance. Migratory birds that traverse the oceans and Gulf of Mexico are especially in need of quality rest stops along the coastal areas where they exit and enter North America. Areas of natural habitat near the coasts are critically important. Landbirds will have consumed much of their energy reserves in crossing long stretches of ocean and need to rest and feed shortly after making landfall. Over 290 species of landbirds cross the Gulf of Mexico in migration. Many of these species in recent years have shown significant declines in their populations.

Most Purple Martins from the eastern United States cross the Gulf of Mexico during migration while the western Purple Martins and some of the mid-western Purple Martins migrate overland. Purple Martins crossing the Gulf of Mexico may fly to the Yucatán Peninsula in Mexico while others may island hop across the Caribbean Sea to South America. Many cross over the Andes Mountains in Venezuela or Columbia and disperse into Brazil. A large part of the population winters in southern Brazil where the birds favor agricultural areas. They feed over the savannahs and fields during the day, consuming large numbers of insects that are agricultural pests. The Amazon River Basin is also a favored wintering site.

Purple Martins gather at night in roosts while they are in Brazil. In Brazil, Purple Martins that hatched in North America mingle in roosts with martin species that spend their entire lives in South America. Many Brazilian martin roosts are located in trees in village plazas. The preference for using village plazas developed in the 1960s. The martins seem to favor areas illuminated with mercury lights. Brazilian conservationists have worked to educate the general public about the value of these insect-eating birds and have been creative in developing ways in which both the Brazilian people and the martins are able to use the same plazas. Conservationists also work to attract the birds to less problematic roost sites.

Adult Purple Martins begin returning to North America when it is still winter there. These early-returning birds are vulnerable to adverse weather, but if they survive they will be assured of obtaining one of the limited number of breeding sites. Cold, or long rainy periods are the leading causes of mortality in the species. Disturbance of roosts, loss of nest sites, competition for nest sites, extreme heat during nesting, impact injury, pesticide poisoning, physical entanglement and harm from European Starlings and European House Sparrows are other leading threats.

The young Purple Martins linger in South America and begin their migration north several weeks after the older birds have left. Many Purple-Martin web sites report the annual return of the species to North America. Visit the web sites for the latest information, news, photographs and videos of Purple Martins. Learn how you can help Purple Martins in your community. Most Purple-Martin organizations have mentoring programs to help those who are interested in hosting a martin colony.

In their international travels, Purple Martins are known by many common names. In Brazil, where the national language is Portuguese, they are called Andorinha Púrpura, the Purple Swallow. In Spanish-speaking nations, they are called Golondrina Grande Negruzca, the Large Black Swallow or Golondrina Azul Americana, the American Blue Swallow.

NATIONAL PURPLE MARTIN SOCIETIES

The Nature Society
(www.naturesociety.org)

Purple Martin Conservation Association (PMCA)
(www.purplemartin.org)

The Purple Martin Society, N.A.
(www.purplemartins.com)

BIBLIOGRAPHIC RESOURCES
(www.purplemartinstory.org)

LEARN ABOUT MIGRATORY BIRDS ONLINE

American Bird Conservancy
(www.abcbirds.org)

American Birding Association
(www.AmericanBirding.org)

Bird Conservation Alliance
(www.BirdConservationAlliance.org)

Birdlife International
(www.birdlife.org)

Cornell Laboratory of Ornithology
(www.birds.cornell.edu)

Environmental Protection Agency
(www.epa.gov/owow/birds/)

Gulf Coast Bird Observatory
(www.gcbo.org)

Journey North
(www.learner.org/jnorth/)

Partners in Flight
(www.partnersinflight.org)

U.S. Fish & Wildlife Service
(www.fws.gov/migratorybirds/)